ECONOMIC
MINERAL DEPOSITS

The Argonauts at Colchis by the Euxine examining the Golden Fleece on which the gold is being collected. (*From Agricola: De Re Metallica.*)

ECONOMIC
MINERAL DEPOSITS

ALAN M. BATEMAN

Silliman Professor of Geology, Yale University
Editor, Economic Geology

Second Edition

JOHN WILEY & SONS, Inc.
New York • London

PRINTED IN THE UNITED STATES OF AMERICA

PREFACE

The first edition of this book appeared at the end of 1942. Since that time war and post-war readjustment has forcibly demonstrated the extent to which the materials of the mineral kingdom constitute the backbone of industrial life and peace-time economic development of nations. Former bountiful supplies now show serious depletion, and nations of the world are looking farther and farther afield for those mineral supplies necessary to their subsistence. This book deals with such mineral deposits, how they are formed, what they are, how and where they occur, and what they are used for. Its chief purpose is as a textbook, designed both for elementary and more advanced courses. The first edition was in demand also as a source of information to all those interested in mineral deposits and in the mineral industry.

The organization of the first edition has been retained. The book is divided into three parts: (I) Principles and Processes, (II) Ore Deposits, and (III) Nonmetallic Mineral Deposits. Each part can be used separately or conjointly. The heart of the book is devoted to the principles and processes of formation of mineral deposits (Part I), and the results of these processes are exemplified in the occurrences described in Parts II and III. For advanced courses Part I can be expanded with contemporaneous collateral assignments chosen from Parts II and III along with other selected readings. The use of the book presupposes some knowledge of general geology and mineralogy.

The treatment of mineral deposits according to processes of formation instead of by a classification of mineral deposits is again followed in this edition. In the author's experience it is more satisfactory from the standpoint of the student and of the field worker as well as for practical considerations of ore finding. Increasing population and increasing mechanization, both in the home and in industry, are making greater and greater demands upon mineral resources and are requiring more scientific methods of exploration for new deposits to replace those being depleted. It is hoped that this book may provide fundamental knowledge for such purposes. For this the author has drawn largely upon his own field studies in many countries of the world, and a large number of the descriptions of the mineral deposits are based upon personal knowledge.

In this edition, as in the former one, magmatic deposits are treated in new detail, as are oxidation and supergene enrichment. Considerable space is devoted to mineral deposits that arise from evaporation and sedimentation; and metamorphism is assigned a place in mineral formation. The chapter on ground water is retained. Statistics are eliminated, in general.

In this revision, the greatest changes have been in Part I. The subchapter on contact metasomatism has had numerous changes, and the term "contact metasomatism" has replaced "contact metamorphism." The former subchapters on replacement and cavity filling have been consolidated under hydrothermal processes, with a new preliminary discussion of hydrothermal processes fundamental to both cavity filling and replacement. The included sections have been much revised and consolidated. The subchapter on sedimentation has been completely rewritten, and much of the material formerly included has been transferred to Parts II and III. The subchapters on residual concentration and mechanical concentration have been consolidated into one subchapter with a preliminary treatment of principles applicable to both. Each of the other chapters has undergone considerable revision for purposes of betterment and to bring the subject matter up to date. The war years brought many new mineral developments and changes, and these have been incorporated. In response to many requests, the selected references at the end of each chapter have been expanded to a total of 41 pages, covering up to the end of 1949. Many new illustrations are included.

For the material presented in this book the author has drawn upon his own field, teaching, government, and editorial experience, and he gratefully acknowledges the heritage of learning of those who have preceded him and of his contemporaries. Since footnotes are omitted, acknowledgments lacking in the text are here recorded with pleasure. His thanks are also due for permission for the use of illustrations, and to those who kindly sent in suggestions for changes.

YALE UNIVERSITY
April, 1950

CONTENTS

ix

CHAPTER 1

INTRODUCTION

Economic geology deals with the materials of the mineral kingdom that man wrests from the earth for his necessities of life and comfort. The search for them has given rise to voyages of discovery and settlement of new lands; their ownership has resulted in commercial or political supremacy or has caused strife and war. In the quest for these mineral substances knowledge of their distribution, character, occurrence, and uses has gradually accumulated, and this knowledge has led to theories regarding their origin. Thus, the subject of mineral deposits developed and as such was taught as one phase of mining in the early mining schools. As greater attention was paid to the rocks that enclosed the ore deposits, to deciphering their character, structure, and origin, and to the land forms developed upon the rocks, the broader science of *geology* gradually arose. Today *economic geology* is a separate branch of geology, as are *mineralogy, petrology, paleontology* and *stratigraphy, structural geology,* and *physiography* or *geomorphology.*

The future of our mineral industry, which is basic to the national economy, rests largely upon the functioning of economic geology for a continued supply of materials. As C. K. Leith expresses it,

With the advent of the industrial revolution in England, a century ago, began the real exploitation of earth materials in a way to influence essentially our material civilization. In this short time, at an ever accelerating rate, minerals have become the fundamental basis of industrialism . . . In these hundred years the production of pig iron has increased 100-fold, of mineral fuels 75-fold, and of copper, 63-fold.

Those countries abundantly supplied with mineral resources became the great industrial nations, and the insatiable demand for minerals to sustain industrialized life has caused the world to dig and consume more minerals within the period embracing the two world wars than in all previous history. Former adequate sources of supply are beginning to look small, and large sources are becoming fewer.

This alarming consumption of our mineral resources and the exhaustion of known reserves means that new supplies must be discovered to take their place if the industry is to persist unimpaired. With waning discovery of obvious mineral outcrops, search must be directed to the less obvious deposits, of which vast numbers must be hidden by the ubiquitous overburden. Every art of geology must be employed to this end, and it promises to become the important work of the economic geologist. In this connection the petroleum geologist has already made an enviable record in the adaptation of geophysical methods and instruments to the discovery of petroleum.

The scope of economic geology includes not only metallic *ore deposits* but the broader field of *nonmetallics,* whose value today is three times that of the metallic ores. In addition, it includes the general application of geology to the uses of man. Thus, it deals with practical problems of the industries and arts, the occurrence of subsurface waters and soils, and the application of geologic principles to important engineering projects. The construction of any large dam, for example, involves questions of the suitability of the foundation rock, of leakage, of subsurface water flow, and of the character and resources of materials that enter into its construction. The subject of economic geology is related also to *geography* and *economics,* since it furnishes information regarding the geographic distribution and resources of the earth materials that are the foundation of the extractive industries.

The early kinship with *mining,* and metal mining in particular, with which economic geology grew up, has persisted, and there is now a specialized subdivision of economic geology known as *mining geology* which deals especially with the problems of ore deposits and their relation to metal mining and, to some extent, with *metallurgy.* This relation may be understood better by considering that the desired metals are locked up in ore minerals, which are admixed with undesired minerals or rock to form ores, and their separation involves the art of metallurgy; the extraction of ores from the ground falls within the realm of mining; and the study of the occurrence, localization, and origin of these ores and their relation to the enclosing rock is the domain of mining geology. The mining geologist functions early in mining operations when he is called upon to determine the probable shape, size, and value of mineral deposits, and particularly their extensions with depth. In addition, he cooperates with the mining engineer during mining operations in the exploration and development of mineral deposits, in finding faulted bodies and in other ways helping to maintain ore reserves, and in the proper location of mine workings to avoid caving ground. In the future he will be called upon more and more to apply geology to mineral finding in districts of waning mines. His knowledge is sought also by the metallurgist to help solve prob-

uriosity nor created specialized knowledge regarding their occurrence.
They were accepted as found, and utilized. Economic geology had
not yet arisen; it was the pre-dawn stage.

EGYPTIAN, GREEK, AND RELATED CULTURES

As the desire for gemstones and metals became more urgent, however, economic geology probably had its inception. Facts of occurrence were noted and recorded; crude theories of origin were evolved;
expeditions were organized for the discovery and exploitation of
deposits; and ownership and barter of these substances became an
important part of the life of the people, even more important relatively
than it is today. The use of gemstones and the mining of them
reached a high art among the early Egyptians, Babylonians, Assyrians,
and Indians. Gemstones were greatly prized, and, living or dead,
the Egyptian was bedecked with jewels, which attained important sig-
ificance among a people obsessed with mysticism. In pre-Dynastic
times (+ 3400 B.C.), it was the color rather than the substance that
the Egyptian prized most. The Theban craftsmen created pleasing
color schemes, utilizing the azure of the lapis lazuli, the red of the
carnelian, the purple of the amethyst, the green of the malachite, the
yellow of the jasper, and the blue of the turquois. He also used agate,
beryl, chalcedony, and garnet and shaped and polished hard stones,
producing not only ovoid but also faceted beads. All these stones except lapis have come from Egypt itself. Even in those remote times
there must have been international barter, since the lapis was probably
obtained from Afghanistan, some 2,400 miles away.

According to Ball, other stones are known to have appeared, such
as onyx in the 2nd Dynasty; azurite and jade in the 3rd Dynasty; and
amber in the 6th Dynasty (2625–2475 B.C.). The stele of Nebona
(18th Dynasty) reads: "I have consecrated numerous gifts in the
temple of my father Osiris in silver in gold in lapis lazuli in copper
and in precious stones." (Ball.) Later, under Greek influence, in the
time of the Ptolemies, several other stones were introduced, including
some Indian gems, such as sapphire, zircon, and topaz.

The oldest form of mining was for gems and decorative stones, and
for over 2,000 years the Pharaohs dispatched expeditions including
engineers and prospectors to the Sinai Peninsula for turquois, and into
the Sudan. Ball identifies as the first economic geologist the Egyptian, Captain Haroeris, who about 2000 B.C. led an expedition to Sinai
and after 3 months' prospecting discovered and extracted large quantities of turquois. The ancient Egyptians (from 1925 B.C.) sank hundreds of shafts for emeralds on the Egyptian coast of the Red Sea;

lems of ore and metal extraction and to obtain suitable ore mixtures
for economical smelting.

Another important subdivision of economic geology is *petroleum
geology*. It deals specifically with the many problems of the location,
occurrence, migration, and origin of petroleum and gas. The petroleum geologist is called upon to determine probable oil-containing
formations, to unravel their structure by geological or geophysical
methods, and to locate prospecting wells. For this purpose he invokes
a knowledge of structural geology, stratigraphy, paleontology, and the
occurrence of petroleum.

These examples indicate the broad scope of economic geology. Since
it deals with the basic materials underlying the extractive industries,
its problems are intertwined with those of diverse industries. It enters
into phases of transportation, international trade, and engineering. It
also embraces many interesting scientific problems in its own field in
which intellectual curiosity plays a greater part than utilitarian problems. The problems of the genesis of different mineral deposits hold
opportunity for long-continued research.

Only certain phases of the broad field of economic geology are
covered in this book, which confines itself largely to mineral deposits
and the principles underlying their occurrence and formation. The
technology of extraction (mining) and treatment (ore dressing and
metallurgy) of the mineral substances are not considered in detail, and
little space is given to statistics. Also the geological features of other
than mineral deposits is beyond the scope of this book. The mineral
substances are not followed far into industry save to indicate their uses.

Of the great variety of mineral substances won from the earth for
the uses of man, coal is the most valuable, followed by metallic minerals, petroleum and natural gas, and other nonmetallic substances
such as clay and gypsum.

For ease in study and ready reference, these materials are divided
in this book into two parts: *metalliferous deposits*, such as gold, copper,
iron, or nickel (Part II); and *nonmetallic substances*, such as coal,
clay, petroleum, or gemstones (Part III). The metalliferous deposits,
or *ore deposits*, are sought for the metals they contain, which are
extracted generally in the metallic state. These deposits are subdivided according to the individual metals. Typical examples are
described in order that their content, occurrence, and origin may be
studied. The nonmetallic, or earthy substances, on the other hand,
are not generally desired for their content of metal but are utilized
principally, after suitable processing, in the form in which they are
extracted. For example, clay is not mined for its aluminum content or

asbestos for its magnesium; but clay is used as a compound in making porcelain or pottery, and asbestos is used as the mineral asbestos. Their physical properties, more than their chemical, for the most part determine their utilization. Both graphite and diamond, for example, consist of carbon, but neither is desired for its carbon content. It is their physical properties that make one a coveted gem and the other a heat- and chemical-resisting substance desired for metallurgical purposes.

There are so many utilized nonmetallic substances of such diverse character and origin that they defy simple classification. For the purpose of this book, however, they are grouped according to their important uses, as, for example, under mineral fuels, ceramic materials, or metallurgical materials. Such an arrangement offers the advantage, for an introductory book, of assembling many diversified materials that have common use under well-known utilitarian groups susceptible of ready reference for both the student of geology and the interested reader. The mode of occurrence and what constitutes workable deposits of these materials will be described under each group.

Economic mineral deposits are geologic bodies that may be worked for one or more minerals or metals. They are exceptional features, sparsely scattered in the rocks or on the earth's surface; they constitute only an infinitesimal part of the earth's crust, but they assume an importance far in excess of their relative volume because of the highly valuable materials they supply to national wealth and industry. They have been concentrated in the rocks under peculiar and exceptional conditions, which it will be our purpose to study. No two mineral deposits are alike in all respects; nevertheless, certain broad principles control their formation. To understand properly how a gold vein or clay deposit has been formed it is necessary to understand first the constitution of mineral deposits and the processes that operate within and upon the earth to form them. Consequently, Part I of this volume is devoted primarily to a general consideration of the principles and processes of the formation of mineral deposits.

General references are found at the end of the book. Selected references are found at the end of each chapter.

CHAPTER 2

BRIEF HISTORY OF THE USE OF MINERA[
THE DEVELOPMENT OF ECONOMIC G[

Ancient Times

Economic geology probably had its inception with t[
zation of mineral products. Long ages must have [
before the early crude knowledge became a craft, late[
a science. The early incentive for the acquisition of [
was undoubtedly utilitarian, but later it was raised t[
plane by the Greek philosophers.

The first earth materials used by primitive man w[
substances — flint, chert, quartz, and certain hard and [
as quartzite, soapstone, or limestone — sought for their [
implements, utensils, and for carving. Clay was wi[
sively used, first for pottery and later for bricks. Unqu[
represents the first large-scale mineral industry, an in[
persisted continuously through the ages. Burned clay [
to be Aurignacian (30,000–20,000 B.C.) have been [
Moravia, and excellent Paleolithic pottery of the S[
(+ 10,000 B.C.) has been found in Egypt. Brick, tile, [
were extensively used by the Chaldeans, Babylonians, a[
tians for building their cities, for irrigation, and for wr[
The early Asiatic and African dwellings were built with [
clay. Later, building stones were extensively used. D[
ing of the pyramids (2980–2925 B.C.) this extractive [
have been on a grand scale, as the Pyramid of Gizeh con[
blocks of stone averaging 2½ tons apiece.

Paleolithic man between 100,000 and 7000 B.C., acco[
Ball, used 13 varieties of minerals — chalcedony, quart[
serpentine, obsidian, pyrite, jasper, steatite, amber, j[
amethyst, and fluorspar. He also utilized ochers or [
At about the time Neolithic man became acquainted [
copper, he also used nephrite, sillimanite, and turquois[
metallic materials are mostly common substances that [
found by accident and whose quest neither greatly stim[

lems of ore and metal extraction and to obtain suitable ore mixtures for economical smelting.

Another important subdivision of economic geology is *petroleum geology.* It deals specifically with the many problems of the location, occurrence, migration, and origin of petroleum and gas. The petroleum geologist is called upon to determine probable oil-containing formations, to unravel their structure by geological or geophysical methods, and to locate prospecting wells. For this purpose he invokes a knowledge of structural geology, stratigraphy, paleontology, and the occurrence of petroleum.

These examples indicate the broad scope of economic geology. Since it deals with the basic materials underlying the extractive industries, its problems are intertwined with those of diverse industries. It enters into phases of transportation, international trade, and engineering. It also embraces many interesting scientific problems in its own field in which intellectual curiosity plays a greater part than utilitarian problems. The problems of the genesis of different mineral deposits hold opportunity for long-continued research.

Only certain phases of the broad field of economic geology are covered in this book, which confines itself largely to mineral deposits and the principles underlying their occurrence and formation. The technology of extraction (mining) and treatment (ore dressing and metallurgy) of the mineral substances are not considered in detail, and little space is given to statistics. Also the geological features of other than mineral deposits is beyond the scope of this book. The mineral substances are not followed far into industry save to indicate their uses.

Of the great variety of mineral substances won from the earth for the uses of man, coal is the most valuable, followed by metallic minerals, petroleum and natural gas, and other nonmetallic substances such as clay and gypsum.

For ease in study and ready reference, these materials are divided in this book into two parts: *metalliferous deposits,* such as gold, copper, iron, or nickel (Part II); and *nonmetallic substances,* such as coal, clay, petroleum, or gemstones (Part III). The metalliferous deposits, or *ore deposits,* are sought for the metals they contain, which are extracted generally in the metallic state. These deposits are subdivided according to the individual metals. Typical examples are described in order that their content, occurrence, and origin may be studied. The nonmetallic, or earthy substances, on the other hand, are not generally desired for their content of metal but are utilized principally, after suitable processing, in the form in which they are extracted. For example, clay is not mined for its aluminum content or asbestos for its magnesium; but clay is used as a compound in making porcelain or pottery, and asbestos is used as the mineral asbestos. Their physical properties, more than their chemical, for the most part determine their utilization. Both graphite and diamond, for example, consist of carbon, but neither is desired for its carbon content. It is their physical properties that make one a coveted gem and the other a heat- and chemical-resisting substance desired for metallurgical purposes.

There are so many utilized nonmetallic substances of such diverse character and origin that they defy simple classification. For the purpose of this book, however, they are grouped according to their important uses, as, for example, under mineral fuels, ceramic materials, or metallurgical materials. Such an arrangement offers the advantage, for an introductory book, of assembling many diversified materials that have common use under well-known utilitarian groups susceptible of ready reference for both the student of geology and the interested reader. The mode of occurrence and what constitutes workable deposits of these materials will be described under each group.

Economic mineral deposits are geologic bodies that may be worked for one or more minerals or metals. They are exceptional features, sparsely scattered in the rocks or on the earth's surface; they constitute only an infinitesimal part of the earth's crust, but they assume an importance far in excess of their relative volume because of the highly valuable materials they supply to national wealth and industry. They have been concentrated in the rocks under peculiar and exceptional conditions, which it will be our purpose to study. No two mineral deposits are alike in all respects; nevertheless, certain broad principles control their formation. To understand properly how a gold vein or clay deposit has been formed it is necessary to understand first the constitution of mineral deposits and the processes that operate within and upon the earth to form them. Consequently, Part I of this volume is devoted primarily to a general consideration of the principles and processes of the formation of mineral deposits.

General references are found at the end of the book. Selected references are found at the end of each chapter.

CHAPTER 2

BRIEF HISTORY OF THE USE OF MINERALS AND OF THE DEVELOPMENT OF ECONOMIC GEOLOGY

Ancient Times

Economic geology probably had its inception with the ancient utilization of mineral products. Long ages must have passed, however, before the early crude knowledge became a craft, later to develop into a science. The early incentive for the acquisition of such knowledge was undoubtedly utilitarian, but later it was raised to an intellectual plane by the Greek philosophers.

The first earth materials used by primitive man were nonmetallic substances — flint, chert, quartz, and certain hard and soft stones such as quartzite, soapstone, or limestone — sought for their use in weapons, implements, utensils, and for carving. Clay was widely and extensively used, first for pottery and later for bricks. Unquestionably clay represents the first large-scale mineral industry, an industry that has persisted continuously through the ages. Burned clay figures believed to be Aurignacian (30,000–20,000 B.C.) have been discovered in Moravia, and excellent Paleolithic pottery of the Solutrean period (+ 10,000 B.C.) has been found in Egypt. Brick, tile, and clay tablets were extensively used by the Chaldeans, Babylonians, and early Egyptians for building their cities, for irrigation, and for writing materials. The early Asiatic and African dwellings were built with bricks made of clay. Later, building stones were extensively used. During the building of the pyramids (2980–2925 B.C.) this extractive industry must have been on a grand scale, as the Pyramid of Gizeh contains 2,300,000 blocks of stone averaging 2½ tons apiece.

Paleolithic man between 100,000 and 7000 B.C., according to S. H. Ball, used 13 varieties of minerals — chalcedony, quartz, rock crystal, serpentine, obsidian, pyrite, jasper, steatite, amber, jadeite, calcite, amethyst, and fluorspar. He also utilized ochers or mineral paints. At about the time Neolithic man became acquainted with gold and copper, he also used nephrite, sillimanite, and turquois. These nonmetallic materials are mostly common substances that probably were found by accident and whose quest neither greatly stimulated human

5

curiosity nor created specialized knowledge regarding their occurrence. They were accepted as found, and utilized. Economic geology had not yet arisen; it was the pre-dawn stage.

EGYPTIAN, GREEK, AND RELATED CULTURES

As the desire for gemstones and metals became more urgent, however, economic geology probably had its inception. Facts of occurrence were noted and recorded; crude theories of origin were evolved; expeditions were organized for the discovery and exploitation of deposits; and ownership and barter of these substances became an important part of the life of the people, even more important relatively than it is today. The use of gemstones and the mining of them reached a high art among the early Egyptians, Babylonians, Assyrians, and Indians. Gemstones were greatly prized, and, living or dead, the Egyptian was bedecked with jewels, which attained important significance among a people obsessed with mysticism. In pre-Dynastic times (+ 3400 B.C.), it was the color rather than the substance that the Egyptian prized most. The Theban craftsmen created pleasing color schemes, utilizing the azure of the lapis lazuli, the red of the carnelian, the purple of the amethyst, the green of the malachite, the yellow of the jasper, and the blue of the turquois. He also used agate, beryl, chalcedony, and garnet and shaped and polished hard stones, producing not only ovoid but also faceted beads. All these stones except lapis have come from Egypt itself. Even in those remote times there must have been international barter, since the lapis was probably obtained from Afghanistan, some 2,400 miles away.

According to Ball, other stones are known to have appeared, such as onyx in the 2nd Dynasty; azurite and jade in the 3rd Dynasty; and amber in the 6th Dynasty (2625–2475 B.C.). The stele of Nebona (18th Dynasty) reads: " I have consecrated numerous gifts in the temple of my father Osiris in silver in gold in lapis lazuli in copper and in precious stones." (Ball.) Later, under Greek influence, in the time of the Ptolemies, several other stones were introduced, including some Indian gems, such as sapphire, zircon, and topaz.

The oldest form of mining was for gems and decorative stones, and for over 2,000 years the Pharaohs dispatched expeditions including engineers and prospectors to the Sinai Peninsula for turquois, and into the Sudan. Ball identifies as the first economic geologist the Egyptian, Captain Haroeris, who about 2000 B.C. led an expedition to Sinai and after 3 months' prospecting discovered and extracted large quantities of turquois. The ancient Egyptians (from 1925 B.C.) sank hundreds of shafts for emeralds on the Egyptian coast of the Red Sea;